8 BLUE BOTTLES ROUND A HONEY JAR.
8 BLUEBOTTLES ROUND A HONEY JAR.

AND IF ONE BLUEBOTTLE GETS SWIPED BY ANGRY PA,
THERE'LL BE 7 BLUEBOTTLES ROUND A HONEY JAR.

7 BLUEBOTTLES NEAR A MURKY SWAMP.
7 BLUEBOTTLES NEAR A MURKY SWAMP.

AND IF ONE BLUEBOTTLE GETS EATEN WITH A CHOMP,
THERE'LL BE 6 BLUEBOTTLES NEAR A MURKY SWAMP.

6 BLUEBOTTLES CIRCLING A BUN.
6 BLUEBOTTLES CIRCLING A BUN.

AND IF ONE BLUEBOTTLE GETS BLASTED BY A GUN,
THERE'LL BE 5 BLUEBOTTLES CIRCLING A BUN.

CONTINUED ON
INSIDE BACK COVER

£3.25

Printed and Published in Great Britain by D. C. THOMSON & CO., LTD., 185 Fleet Street, London, EC4A 2HS.
© D. C. THOMSON & CO., LTD., 1989
ISBN 0-85116-438-2

IT'S AN OLD RECIPE HANDED DOWN FROM MY GREAT GRANNY. THE CONTENTS ARE A DARK SECRET.

WELL, I'M NOT DRINKING IT.

POUR

SIZZLE!

WOW! LOOK WHAT OLIVE'S TEA HAS DONE TO THE PLAYGROUND!

BURST!

SIZZLE!

JUST THINK OF THE WONDERFUL THINGS WE COULD DO WITH A LIQUID THAT BURNS THROUGH STONE . . .

FAR AWAY → LOOK

IT COULD MAKE TUNNELS THROUGH MOUNTAINS.

SQUIRT

SIZZLE

YOU'RE THROUGH!

I'LL NOTE DOWN THE RECIPE AS OLIVE MAKES THE TEA.

LICK

HUBBLE BUBBLE, SOIL AND RUBBLE, TYRES BURN AND CAULDRON BUBBLE!

COOKING POT

EARTH

Soon—

I'VE NOTED DOWN ALL THE INGREDIENTS. WE CAN MAKE THE AMAZING TEA.

And shortly—

URGH! WHAT A SMELL! BUT IT'LL BE WORTH IT!

STIR

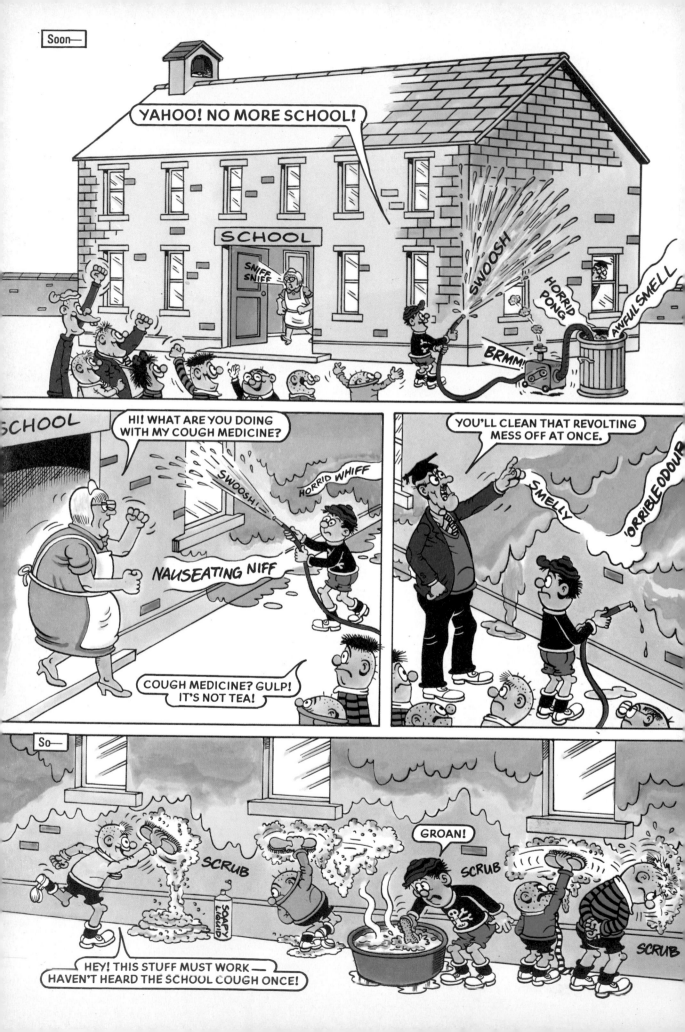

So —

I'LL DELIVER THE MILK THIS WAY.

POUR

Inside the house —

SWOOSH

GLURB!

Later —

HUMPH!

HMM! WONDER WHY DAD'S MADE THAT FUNNY TUBE?

PLOP

GNASTY!

BECAUSE I'VE HAD ENOUGH OF YOU TWO. BYE!

IT'S NICE TO GET A BIT OF PEACE.

PLAY THE "ANIMAL" GAME WITH ME, DAD! GO ON!

RIP!

ERK! I SPOKE TOO SOON! SIGH! I SUPPOSE SO!

HEH! HEH! I'LL BE A SLEEPY, OLD PUSSYCAT.

IN THAT CASE, I'LL BE . . .

. . . A BIG DOGGY!

YIKES!

WOOF! GROWL SNAP!

In the Softy Chalet—

MIRROR, MIRROR ON THE WALL, WHO'S THE SOFTEST OF US ALL?

NO ANSWER. WE'LL HAVE TO ORGANISE A "MISTER SUPER-SOFT CONTEST" TO FIND THE ANSWER.

So—

WONDERFUL WIMP →

LOOK AT THE LOVELY FIRST PRIZE.

OOO! SIMPLY SUPER.

VERY HARD SUM BOOK

Next—

LOOK AT THIS PRETTY BUTTERFLY SHAPED BEDJACKET I CROTCHETED.

SUPER!

I CROTCHETED A BUTTERFLY BEDJACKET, TOO . . .

SMUG →

. . . FOR FLUTTER, MY SWEET LITTLE CHUM!

FLAP

FLAP

Soon—

THIS IS A SUPER SCULPTURE, REX.

CHIP CHIP

But—

OF COURSE, I DON'T SCULPT WITH STONE — IT'S MUCH TOO TOUGH. I ONLY USE COTTON WOOL.

OOO! SUPER SOFT.

Then—

LORD SNOOTY

MINNIE the MINX

I'M OFF OUT FOR A WALK, PARENTS.

YAHOO! HOORAY! PEACE AND QUIET FOR A WHILE.

CAN YOU READERS HEAR SOMETHING? THE TRAMPING OF FEET FOR INSTANCE.

TRAMP! TRAMP!

WONDER WHAT IT IS?

FOOD! OOYAH!

GOTTIM!

In the park—

GET YOUR LOVELY BALLOONS HERE!

I'LL HAVE ONE!

WAAH!

DID I TELL YOU IT'S FULL OF HOT AIR?

SHRIEK!

KNEW THESE DIVING BOOTS WOULD COME IN HANDY SOMEDAY.

HELP! MUMSY!

DON'T WORRY. I'LL GET YOU DOWN.

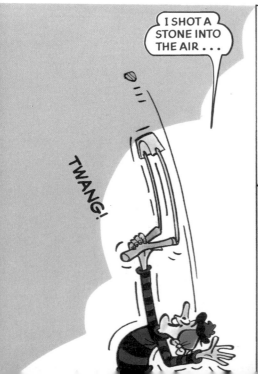

I SHOT A STONE INTO THE AIR . . .

TWANG!

BANG!

. . . SHE FELL TO EARTH . . .

GREEDY BEA

If you go down in the woods today,
You'd better go in disguise.

If you go down in the woods today,
You're sure of a big surprise.

Today's the day the greedy bears
nick your picnic!

Picnic time for greedy bears,
Those naughty greedy bears are after
your lovely grub today.

Then, with a gleeful shout,
They'll leap on you unawares.

At six o'clock his Mummy and Daddy
Will take Ted home to bed,

or three fat bears are up to no good —

— Their aim in life to snaffle your food.

izzas, pies and choc eclairs —
hey'd surely love to stuff the lot away.

See them slyly sneak about,

Extremely plump and contented bears.

WE'LL PUT A STOP TO IT, THOUGH.

WHEE!

RIGHT LET'S MOVE THE STRAW!

WILL'S MUM →

SNIFFLE!

I'LL DO A LITTLE SWINGING . . .

I HATE DOING THE HOUSEWORK.

I KNOW . . .

. . . I'LL USE GRAN'S BOOK OF SPELLS AND MAKE THE HOUSE DO THE WORK!

So —

HERE IT IS!

FIZZY, TIZZY — LET'S GET BUSY!

YIKES! THIS ISN'T WORKING!

Later —

GASP! WHAT'S HAPPENED HERE? WHERE'S BORIS?

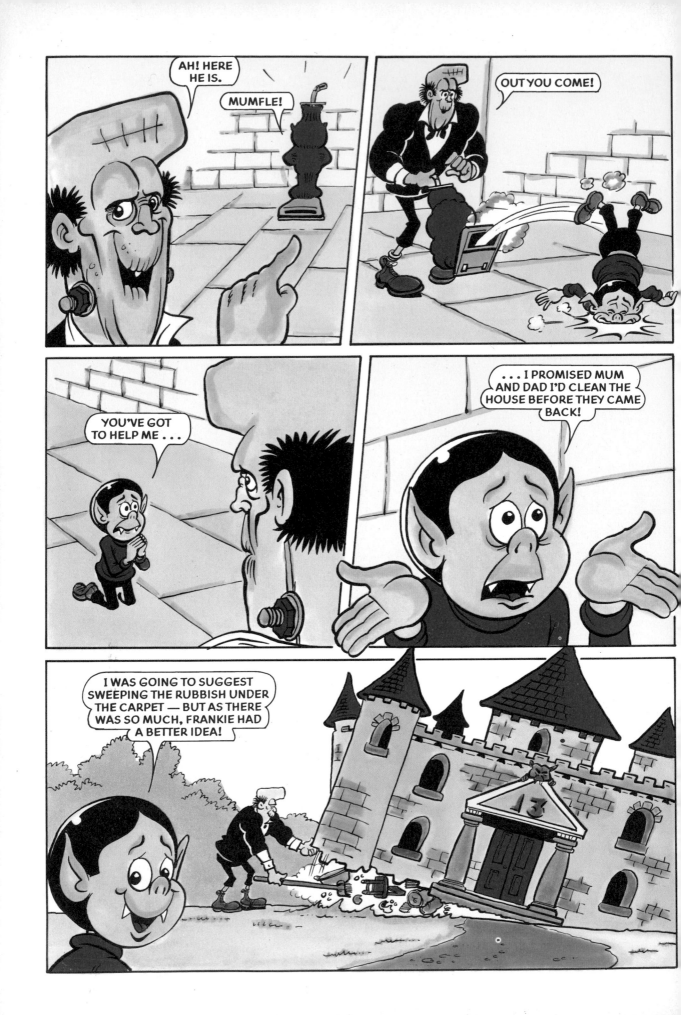

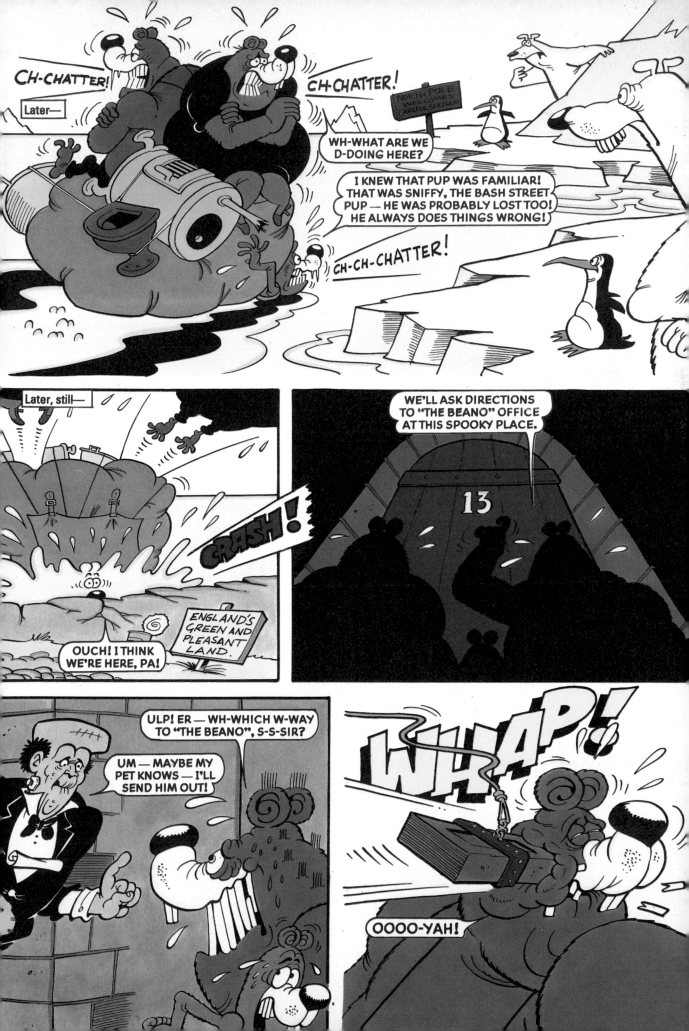

DUH-H! NO, SABRE, MY PET BRICK, DOESN'T KNOW — MAYBE LITTLE TIDDLES DOES.

WH-WHO IS TIDDLES, WHEN HE'S AT HOME?

OUR PET PUSSYCAT!

YES — ER — WELL, WE'LL F-FIND OUR OWN WAY . . .

. . . GOODBYEEEEEEEEEEE!

F-FASTER, T-T-TED!

VROOOM-M

SLAM!

NOBODY KEEPS A HUNGRY PA FROM HIS GRUB!

LISTEN, TOSH — WE WANT THE SAME GRUB AS YOU . . .

ULP!

PULL!

. . . AND WE WANT IT NOW!

IF Y-YOU INSIST! OUR CHEF'S ABOUT TO SERVE LUNCH!

DOOOF!

DANNY'S NANNY

Little Danny Wilson has a very unusual Nanny. She has a long nose, four legs, a tail and a funny coat. You see, Danny's Nanny is a dog!

TIME FOR YOUR AFTERNOON NAP, DANNY!

THROW

I WON'T GO TO SLEEP, NANNY . .

. . . UNLESS I GET A STORY!

HUMPH! DOG'S CAN'T READ, SO . . .

LITTLE RED RIDING-HOOD

ABANDON HOPE ALL WHO ENTER

BUT ALSO IN THE FOREST WAS A WICKED WOLF!

So —

Wolf-type sounds. →

SNARL! GROWL!

MAN! THE D IS A BRUTE

NOW AS LITTLE RED RIDING HOOD . . .

CUE LITTLE R. RIDING HOOD

EH?

PHEW! PANT! HARD GOING THIS QUICK CHANGE ACT!

. . . AHEM! WAITED AT THE DOOR OF GRANDMA'S COTTAGE IN THE WOOD . . .

WHEEZE! PHEW! GASP!

. . . ALONG CAME THE WICKED WOLF! HA-HA-HA!

SNARL! PUFF! PANT! GROWL! WHEEZE!

WOW!

SCOOSH!

ZOOM!

CHUG A-CHUG

HUH! HE WASHED THE WORDS OFF — I'VE GOT ANOTHER IDEA, PALS!

Soon —

HERE'S TEACHER NOW.

GET THE ROPE READY!

GOT HIM!

TUG

TRIP

TUG

OW!

SPLAT!

AND THEY'RE OFF IN THE IVY STEEPLECHASE!

GALLOP!

LEAP!

EEK!

AND BRISTLY BOY'S OVER THE FIRST FENCE.

But —

HUMPH!

CRASH!

CLATTER!

JUST A MINUTE, IVY!

OHO!

STOMP

BALL BOY

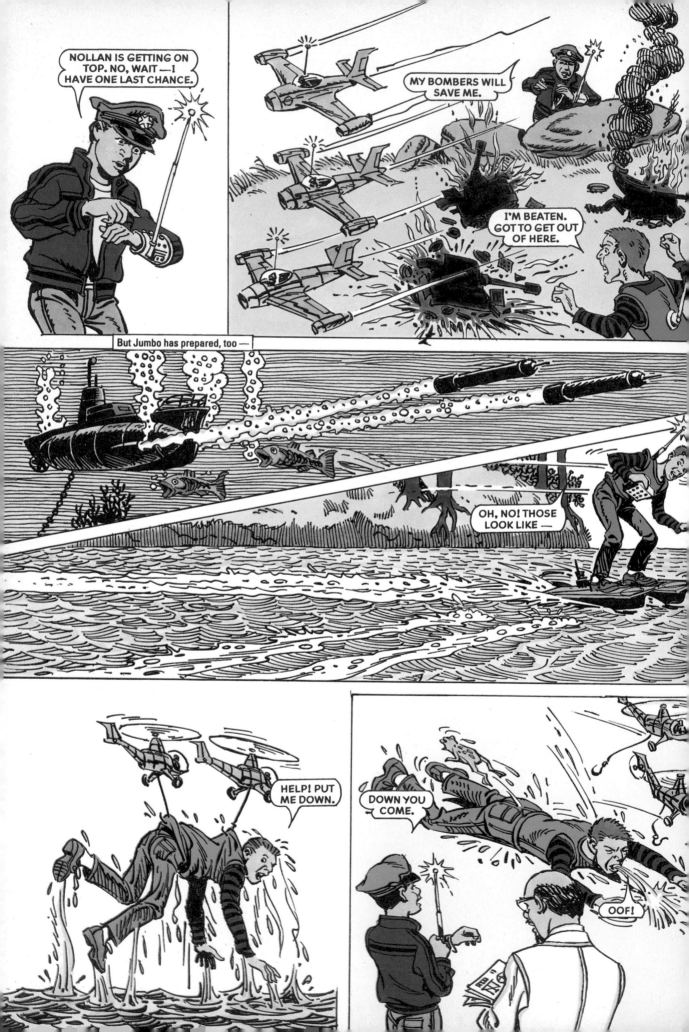

DID YOU HEAR ABOUT THE STUPID GHOST? HE CLIMBED OVER WALLS!
WHAT'S GOT WEBBED FEET AND FANGS? *COUNT QUACKULA!*
WHAT'S A GARGOYLE? *SOMETHING YOU TAKE FOR A SORE THROAT!*
MUM, WHAT'S A VAMPIRE?
SHUT UP AND EAT YOUR SOUP BEFORE IT CLOTS.

DENNIS the MENACE

MY FOOTBALL'S FLAT AND MY PUMP DOESN'T PUMP! SIGH!

HMMM!

Soon —

I'M LATE FOR MY YEARLY MEDICAL CHECK AT THE DOCTOR'S.

ZOOM

WAH! MY TYRE'S FLAT! HOW DID IT GET FLAT? HOW WILL I GET TO THE DOCTOR'S ON TIME?

THUD! THUD!

SCREECH TO HALT!

SO — THOUGHT YOU'D HIDE UP THERE, ROGER!

SNARL! I'D KNOW THAT JUMPER ANYWHERE!

But —

SHAKE!

SHAKE!

EH?

HO-HO! ONLY OLD CLOTHES!

Later —

HMM! THERE'S A DODGE TO BE WORKED HERE!

OUT YOU COME, FIDO!

I'LL PUT ON MY OLD CLOTHES FIRST!

Suddenly —

SPLAT!

SHAKE-SHAKE!

OH! FIDO!

YOU POOR BOY! I HOPE THAT MUDDY WATER DOESN'T RUIN YOUR CLOTHES. HAVE THEM CLEANED.

THANK YOU!

NAUGHTY BOY, FIDO!

WAHEY! DODGE 445 WORKED A TREAT!

So —

NOW TO WAIT FOR THE CLOTHES TO DRY THEN DODGE SOME MORE!

GRR!

ROGER!

ULP! BASHER!

ZOO

RUN FOR IT!

COME BACK TILL I BASH YOU!

HMM! DODGE HATCHING HERE!

CHIMPS TEA PARTY

AHA! YOU REALLY ARE UP IN THE TREES THIS TIME, ROGER!

CHORTLE!

HUMPH! ROGER!

YES — SPARE CLOTHES CAN BE HANDY FOR GETTING YOU OUT OF TROUBLE!

WAY OUT

QUITE SO, ROGER. SINCE YOU SENT CHARLIE CHIMP OFF TO BE CHASED BY YOUR 'PAL' — YOU'LL HAVE TO TAKE HIS PLACE AT THE TEA PARTY!

OH, NO! A MONKEY SUIT!

HUMPH! MAYBE NOT SUCH A GOOD IDEA — SPARE CLOTHES!

CHORTLE!